# Mystery Mob
## and the
## Mummy's Curse

Roger Hurn

Illustrated by
*Stik*

RISING

**Rising Stars UK Ltd.**
22 Grafton Street, London W1S 4EX
www.risingstars-uk.com

The right of Roger Hurn to be identified as the author of this work
has been asserted by him in accordance with the Copyright,
Design and Patents Act 1988.

Published 2007
Reprinted 2008

Cover design: Button plc
Illustrator: Stik, Bill Greenhead for Illustration
Text design and typesetting: Andy Wilson
Publisher: Gill Budgell
Publishing manager: Sasha Morton
Editor: Catherine Baker
Series consultant: Cliff Moon

British Library Cataloguing in Publication Data.
A CIP record for this book is available from the British Library

ISBN: 978-1-84680-224-9

Printed in the UK by CPI Bookmarque, Croydon, CR0 4TD

# Contents

# Meet the Mystery Mob

**Name:**

Gummy

**FYI:** Gummy hasn't got much brain – and even fewer teeth.

**Loves:** Soup.

**Hates:** Toffee chews.

**Fact:** The brightest thing about him is his shirt.

**Name:**

Lee

**FYI:** If Lee was any cooler he'd be a cucumber.

**Loves:** Hip-hop.

**Hates:** Hopscotch.

**Fact:** He has his own designer label (which he peeled off a tin).

**Name:**

Rob

**FYI:** Rob lives in his own world – he's just visiting planet Earth.

**Loves:** Daydreaming.

**Hates:** Nightmares.

**Fact:** Rob always does his homework – he just forgets to write it down.

**Name:**

Dwayne

**FYI:** Dwayne is smarter than a tree full of owls.

**Loves:** Anything complicated.

**Hates:** Join-the-dots books.

**Fact:** If he was any brighter you could use him as a floodlight at football matches.

**Name:**

Chet

**FYI:** Chet is as brave as a lion with steel jaws.

**Loves:** Having adventures.

**Hates:** Knitting.

**Fact:** He's as tough as the chicken his granny cooks for his tea.

**Name:**

Adi

**FYI:** Adi is as happy as a football fan with tickets to the big match.

**Loves:** Telling jokes.

**Hates:** Moaning minnies.

**Fact:** He knows more jokes than a jumbo joke book.

# Tut's Treasure

The Mystery Mob are really excited.
A museum in Egypt has sent their
local museum a fantastic display
called 'King Tut's Treasures'.

King Tut ruled Egypt thousands
of years ago. He became king
when he was only ten years old.
The boys think this is *so* cool.
They're looking at King Tut's
gold burial mask, which is inside
a glass case.

**Dwayne**   King Tut's gold mask
is worth loads of money.

**Gummy**   I bet someone tries to steal it.

**Lee**   No way. It's protected
by a mummy's curse.

**Rob**   That's right. And King Tut's mum
is one scary lady.

**Dwayne**   Don't be daft! The mummy's
not King Tut's mum.
A mummy is a dead body
that the Ancient Egyptians
wrapped up in bandages.

**Rob**   Ugh! That's gross.

**Chet**   Yes, but do you think a mummy
really does curse you
if you try to steal the gold?

**Lee**   I don't know – it's a mystery.

**Adi**  Hey, I've got a mummy mystery for you lot to solve.

**Mystery Mob**

What is it?

**Adi**  What do you get if you cross a man who fixes car horns with an Egyptian king?

**Mystery Mob**

Er … no idea.

**Adi**  A *toot and car man!*

**Chet**     Adi, if you make any more jokes
             like that, the mummy will
             be cursing us – not the thief!

**Dwayne**   So do us a favour, Adi
             and make like a mummy.

**Adi**      What do you mean?

**Mystery Mob**

             Just wrap up!

# No Entry

The boys wander off to look at the rest
of the museum. Rob and Lee decide to go
to the museum shop. On the way they see
some spooky stone steps going down
to a dark cellar door. A 'No Entry' sign
is at the top of the steps.

**Rob**    I wonder what's down
in that cellar.

**Lee**    It must be the stuff they
don't dare to put on display
in the museum.

**Rob**    Right. So is that why
they've put up the big
'No Entry' sign?

**Lee**    Exactly. I reckon
there's something in that cellar
that the museum people
don't want us to see.

**Rob**    Wow. Maybe it's the mummy
who cursed King Tut's gold.

**Lee**    (snapping his fingers)
You've got it!

The two boys stare at each other.

**Rob**      Hey, I dare you to go down
into the cellar and take a look.

**Lee**      OK. I'll do it ... why not?

**Rob**      Duh, because there's like
a totally scary mummy in there,
that's why not.

**Lee**    No, think about it. The mummy only curses thieves who try to steal King Tut's gold, right?

**Rob**    Right.

**Lee**    Well, we're not going to steal the gold, so we'll be safe. It won't chase after us.

**Rob**    But what if we make it angry?

**Lee**    We won't. We'll sneak in,
have a quick peek at it
and then tiptoe back out.
It won't even know we're there.

**Rob**    If you say so.

**Lee**    I do. Oh man, the others
are going to be well upset
when they find out
that we saw the mummy
and they didn't.

# Snakes Alive!

The boys tiptoe down the spooky
stone steps. They stop at the dark
cellar door. They listen at the keyhole
but they don't hear a sound.
Lee reaches out and turns
the door handle. The door creaks open.

**Rob**  Ssshhh! We don't want
the mummy to hear us.

**Lee**  It won't – as long as you
keep quiet. Now where is it?

**Rob**  I don't know. Perhaps
it's hiding in the shadows.
I can't see anything
except these creepy
mummy coffins.

**Lee**    I bet it's inside one of the coffins.

**Rob**    But which one?

**Lee**    I've got no idea. Why don't you open one and see?

The boys hear something moving
in a dark corner of the cellar.
They freeze. The sound is coming
from behind a pile of boxes.

**Rob**    (whispering) I've got
a better idea.

**Lee**    (whispering) What's that?

**Rob**    (shouting) Let's get out of here!

The two boys dash for the door.
But Rob pulls too hard on the handle
and it comes off in his hand.

**Lee**    Oh, well done, Rob.
       Now we're trapped in this cellar
       with a mad mummy.

**Rob**    No, we're not.

**Lee**  Earth to Rob – we are.

**Rob**  No … we're trapped in this cellar
with a great big snake.

A large cobra slithers out
from the shadows. Its eyes glitter
as it sways in front of them.

**Lee**      It must have slipped inside
one of the boxes
when the treasure
was sent over from Egypt.

**Rob**      Why would it do that?

**Lee**      I guess it was looking
for a comfy place to sleep.
There's lots of soft straw
in these boxes
to keep the treasure safe.

**Rob**  OK … but what did it eat?

**Lee**  Cobras can go for ages
without eating.
But now it's arrived,
it's woken up –
and it looks hungry to me.

**Rob**  And we look like food to it!

Things are looking bad for Rob and Lee.
Are they going to end up as a snack
for a snake?

# Plan B

**Lee**    Hey, good news. Did you know
snakes can only look
at one thing at a time?

**Rob**    Yes, but the one thing
this snake's looking at is me.

**Lee**    Exactly. So you just stand still
and let it look while I sneak away.

**Rob**    That's a great plan. Er …
but when do I sneak away?

**Lee**    You don't.

**Rob**    Right! Um … I don't think
I like this plan any more.

**Lee**    That's because you
haven't heard it all yet.

**Rob**    So tell me.

**Lee** I'm going to grab that broom
over there. Then I'm going
to creep up behind the cobra
and pin him down with it. Sorted!

**Rob** But what if the cobra
gets fed up with looking at me
before you get him
with the broom?

**Lee**    We try Plan B.

**Rob**    What's Plan B?

**Lee**    I don't know. But don't panic.
         I'll tell you what it is
         as soon as I think it up.

Lee gives Rob a big smile and thumbs up.
Rob's heart sinks.

# Best Friends

While Rob stands and shakes,
the snake sways and stares.
Lee slips away. The cobra takes no notice
of him. It only has eyes for Rob.

Lee goes to the wall and picks up
the broom. He swings round with it.
But he is in too much of a hurry.
The broom bashes into
an old mummy coffin.

The coffin wobbles, and the door
of the mummy case swings open.

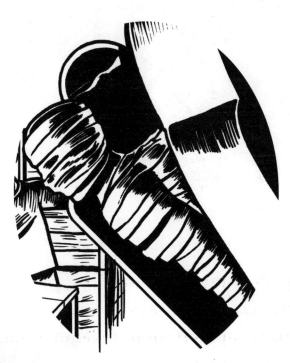

**Lee**    Oh no, what have I done?

**Rob**    (shouting) You've only gone
and annoyed the snake,
you idiot! It's going to get
me now!

The snake rises up. It's just about to
strike at Rob. Then, all of a sudden,
a very large mummy topples out
of the coffin and falls on top of the snake.

The cobra is not hurt, but it is
trapped. It can't escape from
underneath the mummy.
The boys are safe.

**Lee**    See, I told you not to panic. Plan B worked out just fine.

**Rob**    Was that Plan B then?

**Lee**    Oh yes. I used the mummy to save you because I knew there was no way the cobra could hurt the mummy.

**Rob**     Why? Because it's all wrapped up
in bandages?

**Lee**     No – because it's been dead
for thousands of years.

Rob gives Lee a hard look.
Then he shrugs.

**Rob**    Well, I guess this teaches me one lesson.

**Lee**    What's that?

**Rob**    The best person to get you out of trouble is not your best mate – it's your mummy.

# About the author

Roger Hurn has:

 been an actor in 'The Exploding Trouser Company'

 played bass guitar in a rock band

been given the title Malam Oga (wise teacher, big boss!) while on a storytelling trip to Africa.

Now he's a writer, and he hopes you like reading about the Mystery Mob as much as he likes writing about them.

# The Egyptian mummy quiz

**Questions**

1 What did the mummy say when he was cross with the skeleton?

2 In which room in your house will you never find a mummy?

3 Why does a mummy go on holiday?

4 Why don't mummies tell secrets?

5 What do you call a mummy who eats biscuits in bed?

6 Who changed King Tut's nappies when he was a baby?

7 What did the Egyptian boy say when he was scared?

8 Why do mummies like hip-hop?

**Answers**

1 I've got a bone to pick with you!
2 The living room.
3 To unwind.
4 Because they keep things under wraps.
5 A crummy mummy.
6 His mummy.
7 I want my mummy!
8 Because they are great wrappers.

## How did you score?

🖐 If you got all eight mummy answers correct, then you are dead clever!

🖐 If you got six mummy answers correct, your mummy will be really proud of you.

🖐 If you got fewer than four mummy answers correct, then you are in danger of becoming unwrapped.

41

# When I was a kid

**Question**   Did you ever go to a museum when you were a kid?

**Roger**   Yes. My teacher took my class on a museum trip.

**Question**   Did you find any of the Ancient Egyptian mummies scary?

**Roger**   No, but the Ancient Egyptian daddies were terrifying!

**Question**   What was your favourite bit of the trip?

**Roger**   When some kids from another school tried to draw our teacher.

**Question**   Why did they do that?

**Roger**   Well, he was so old they thought he was one of the exhibits.

# Adi's favourite mummy joke

Where do mummies go swimming?

In the Dead Sea!

# How to have a great Egyptian Mummy museum visit

Before you go, check out some basic facts about the Ancient Egyptians.
It'll help you tell your mummies from your deadies!

*Think of some questions that you want to know the answers to. For example, how long does it take a mummy to get dressed in the morning?*

Always go to the toilet before you start your museum tour – those ancient mummies can be pretty scary!

*Actually, you needn't be frightened of the mummies – they haven't got the guts to hurt you!*

Don't chat to the mummies –
they'll start to relax and unwind!

 *If you see the number 1267 BC
written on the side of a mummy's coffin
that's the date he died – not the number
of the car that ran him over!*

 So, enjoy your Egyptian mummy
museum visit but, whatever you do,
don't call King Tut's mummy
a golden mouldy. It just winds him up!

# Fantastic facts about Ancient Egypt

1 Coffins in Ancient Egypt usually had an eye painted on the side. This was so the mummy could keep an eye on you!

2 The Ancient Egyptians loved cats. If a pet cat died its owners shaved off their eyebrows to show how upset they were.

3 Egyptian priests had all their body hair removed – even their eyelashes! They were a bunch of smoothies!

4 Mummies are wrapped in over ten layers of linen. No wonder mummies find it hard to unwind!

5 In Ancient Egypt, people thought it brought good luck if you stepped into a house using your left foot first. Mind you, it was bad luck if you stubbed your toe!

# Museum lingo

**Ancient artefact** Something from a very long time ago – please don't call your granddad this.

**Attendant** A person who sits guarding the displays. Do not poke them with your finger as they are real and not waxwork figures.

**Interactive display** A 'hands on' exhibition. But if you want to get your hands on King Tut's treasure – think again.

**Mummy case** A box with an embalmed body inside – not the thing your mum packs when she's going on holiday.

**Museum collection** Objects from the past that the museum has put on show – not a bunch of museums.

# Mystery Mob

## Mystery Mob Set 1:

Mystery Mob and the Abominable Snowman
Mystery Mob and the Big Match
Mystery Mob and the Circus of Doom
Mystery Mob and the Creepy Castle
Mystery Mob and the Haunted Attic
Mystery Mob and the Hidden Treasure
Mystery Mob and the Magic Bottle
Mystery Mob and the Missing Millions
Mystery Mob and the Monster on the Moor
Mystery Mob and the Mummy's Curse
Mystery Mob and the Time Machine
Mystery Mob and the UFO

## Mystery Mob Set 2:

Mystery Mob and the Ghost Town
Mystery Mob and the Bonfire Night Plot
Mystery Mob and the April Fools' Day Joker
Mystery Mob and the Great Pancake Race
Mystery Mob and the Scary Santa
Mystery Mob and the Conker Conspiracy
Mystery Mob and the Top Talent Contest
Mystery Mob and Midnight at the Waxworks
Mystery Mob and the Runaway Train
Mystery Mob and the Wrong Robot
Mystery Mob and the Day of the Dinosaurs
Mystery Mob and the Man Eating Tiger

# RISING ★ STARS

**Mystery Mob books are available from most booksellers.**

**For mail order information
please call Rising Stars on 0871 47 23 010
or visit www.risingstars-uk.com**